HYMN PRELUDES
for the Church Year Book 1

Feasts & Festivals

Kevin
Mayhew

We hope you enjoy *Hymn Preludes for the Church Year*
Book 1: Feasts and Festivals
Further copies of this and our many other books are available
from your local Kevin Mayhew stockist.

In case of difficulty, please contact the publisher direct by writing to:

The Sales Department
KEVIN MAYHEW LTD
Buxhall
Stowmarket
Suffolk IP14 3BW

Phone 01449 737978
Fax 01449 737834
E-mail info@kevinmayhewltd.com

Please ask for our complete catalogue of outstanding Organ Music.

First published in Great Britain in 2001 by Kevin Mayhew Ltd.

© Copyright 2001 Kevin Mayhew Ltd.

ISBN 1 84003 698 2
ISMN M 57004 830 4
Catalogue No: 1400273

0 1 2 3 4 5 6 7 8 9

Cover design: Jonathan Stroulger
Music setter: Rob Danter
Proof reader: Sally Gough

Printed and bound in Great Britain

Contents

Page

LENT AND HOLY WEEK

EASTER AND ASCENSION

PENTECOST

TRINITY

About the Composers

Malcolm Archer (*b.*1952) is Organist and Master of the Choristers at Wells Cathedral. He is conductor of Wells Oratorio Society and the City of Bristol Choir, in addition to his work as a composer and recitalist.

Rosalie Bonighton (*b.*1946) is a recitalist, teacher and composer with a special interest in writing music for new liturgical needs.

Paul Bryan is Director of Music and Organist of St John's College School, Cambridge and conductor of the Walmisley Singers.

Andrew Fletcher (*b.*1950) is a teacher, composer, accompanist and recitalist, performing regularly all over the world.

Dr A. E. Floyd (1877-1974) was Director of Music at St Paul's Cathedral in Melbourne for thirty-two years and one of the great personalities of Australian music.

Andrew Gant (*b.*1963) is Director of Music in Chapel at Selwyn College, Cambridge, and Organist and Master of the Choir at the Royal Military Chapel (The Guards Chapel), Wellington Barracks, London.

Colin Hand (*b.*1929) is composer of choral, orchestral and chamber music for both professional and amateur players. He spent many years as a teacher, lecturer and examiner.

John Jordan (*b.*1941) was for many years Master of the Music at Chelmsford Cathedral. He now combines being Music Director of St Margaret's Priory Church, King's Lynn, and Director of Music at the national shrine of Our Lady of Walsingham.

Richard Lloyd (*b.*1933) was Assistant Organist of Salisbury Cathedral and successively Organist of Hereford and Durham Cathedrals. He now divides his time between examining and composing.

William Lloyd Webber (1914-1982) was Director of the London College of Music, and Professor at the Royal College of Music. As well as being renowned as a brilliant organist he also composed music in many different spheres.

John Marsh (*b.*1939) formerly Organist and Director of Music at St Mary Redcliffe Church, Bristol, is now a member of the music staff at Clifton College, Bristol.

Colin Mawby (*b.*1936) was previously Choral Director at Radio Telefis Éireann, the national broadcasting authority in the Republic of Ireland, and Master of the Music at Westminster Cathedral. He is Conductor of Ireland's only full-time professional choir, the National Chamber Choir of Ireland.

Andrew Moore (*b.*1954) is a Benedictine priest. He studied at the Royal Academy of Music and at Cambridge University, and is now parish priest of Lambourn and Hungerford.

Philip Moore (*b.*1943) is Organist and Master of the Music at York Minster.

June Nixon is Organist and Director of the Choir at St Paul's Cathedral, Melbourne, Australia. She also teaches at the Melbourne University School of Music.

Richard Proulx (*b.*1937) is a composer, conductor and organist. He was Music Director at the Cathedral of the Holy Name in Chicago for fourteen years. His ensemble 'The Cathedral Singers' is well known for its series of recordings of both early music and original works.

Noel Rawsthorne (*b.*1929) was Organist of Liverpool Cathedral for twenty-five years and City Organist and Artistic Director at St George's Hall, Liverpool. He was also Senior Lecturer in Music at St. Katherine's College, Liverpool, until his retirement in 1993. In 1994 he was awarded an honorary degree of Doctor of Music by the University of Liverpool.

Alan Ridout has composed music in almost every form: symphonies, chamber music, choral and instrumental works. His music is widely performed all over the world.

Betty Roe (*b.*1930) studied at the Royal Academy of Music and later with Lennox Berkeley. She composes in many forms from solo songs to operas.

Martin Setchell (*b.*1949) is an English-born and trained musician, choral conductor and organ recitalist now working in New Zealand, where he is a Senior Lecturer in Music at the University of Canterbury in Christchurch and Organist at the Christchurch Town Hall.

Richard Shephard (*b.*1949) is Headmaster of the Minster School, York, and Vicar Choral in York Minster. He has served on the Archbishops' Commission on Church Music and on the Archbishops' Commission on Cathedrals.

Christopher Tambling (*b.*1964) is Director of Music at Downside School and Master of the Schola Cantorum of Downside Abbey. He was previously Director of Music at Glenalmond College and Perth City Organist.

Quentin Thomas (*b.*1972) is a member of the teaching staff at the Oratory School, Woodcote, Berkshire. He is also active as a conductor, performer and composer.

Stanley Vann (*b.*1910) was successively Organist at Chelmsford and Peterborough Cathedrals.

Alan Viner (*b.*1951) was formerly Director of Music at the Priory Boy's Grammar School, Shrewsbury, and the Wakeman School, Shrewsbury. He now devotes his time to private teaching, composing and accompanying.

Norman Warren (*b.*1934) is a retired Archdeacon of Rochester. He is well known as a composer of hymns, and was a member of the music committee for *Hymns for Today's Church*.

Advent

CROSS OF JESUS

Andrew Fletcher

Andante doloroso (♩ = 52)

Sw.

rall.

dim.

FRANCONIA

Andrew Fletcher

Gt. 8' + Sw.
Sw. 8' 4'
Ped. 16' + Gt., Sw.

Andante tranquillo (♩ = c. 60)

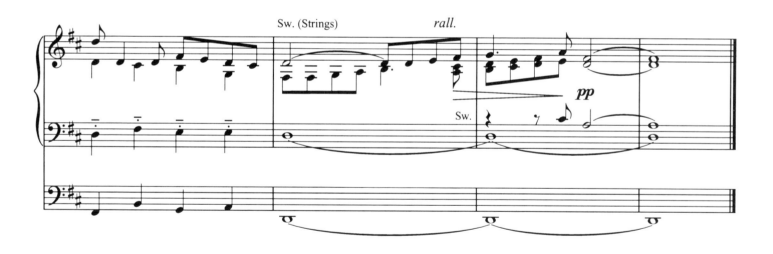

HALTON HOLGATE

Philip Moore

un poco rall.

MERTON

Malcolm Archer

VENI EMMANUEL

Noel Rawsthorne

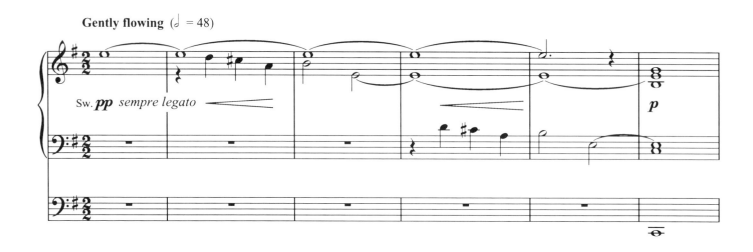

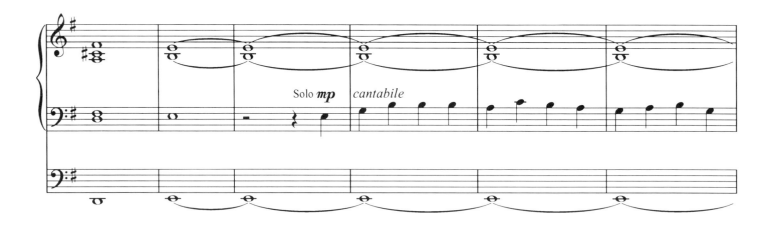

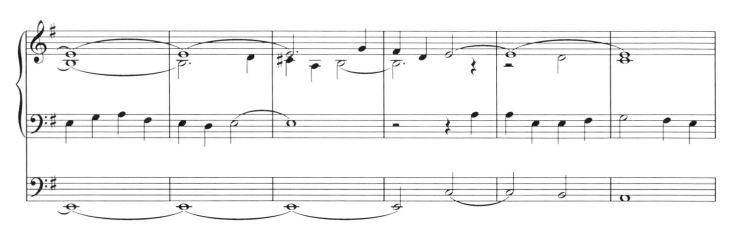

Grandioso

fff

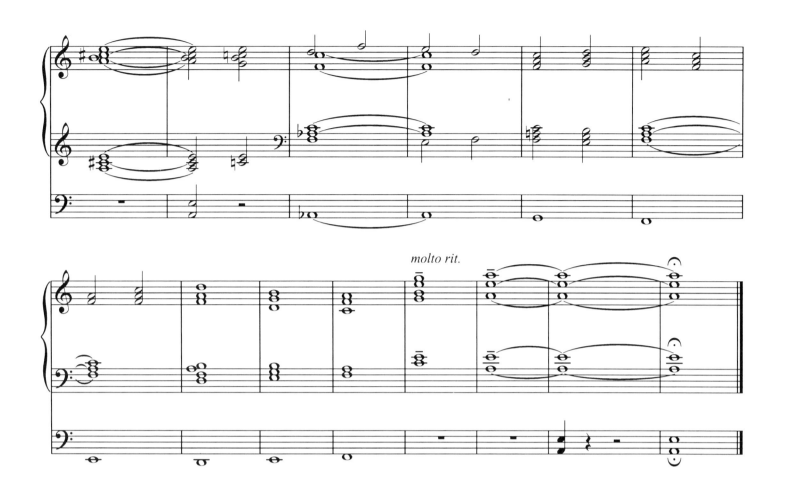

VENI EMMANUEL

Andrew Moore

WACHET AUF

Rosalie Bonighton

poco rit. a tempo

($\flat$ = $\flat$) rall.

29

WINCHESTER NEW

Malcolm Archer

Christmas & Epiphany

ADESTE FIDELES

Noel Rawsthorne

poco a poco allargando

37

BIRJINA GAZTETTOBAT ZEGOEN

Noel Rawsthorne

With a gentle lilt ($\boldsymbol{\cdot}$. = 48)

mp

poco a poco dim.

pp

BRANSLE DE L'OFFICIAL

Noel Rawsthorne

44

Optional
repeat

poco rall.

BRANSLE DE L'OFFICIAL

Christopher Tambling

Brightly: detached

BUNESSAN

Andrew Moore

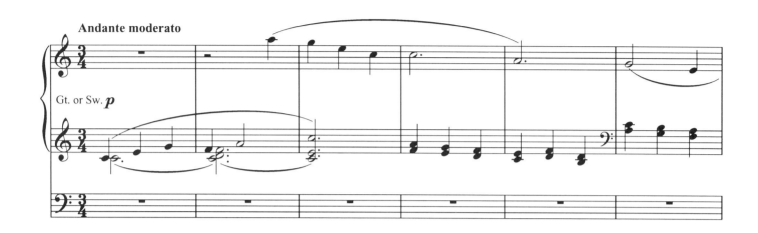

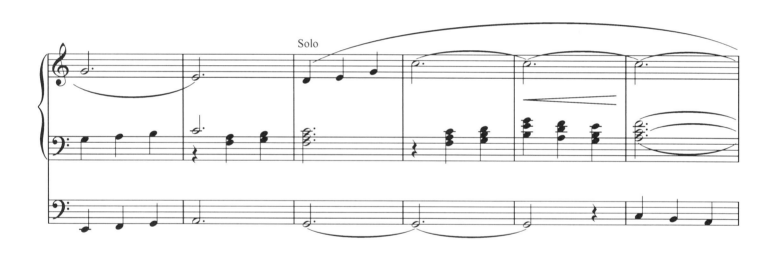

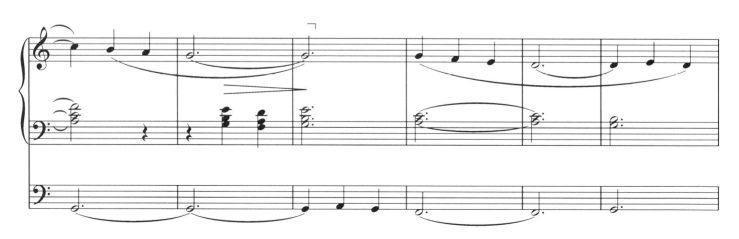

CORDE NATUS

Malcolm Archer

Grandly, but with movement (♩ = 104)

CORDE NATUS

Philip Moore

un poco rall.

for Guy Oldham

COVENTRY CAROL

Betty Roe

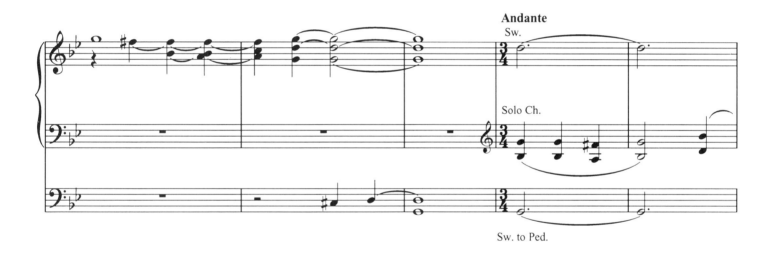

for Sophie's second Christmas

CRADLE SONG

Richard Lloyd

poco rall.

Meno mosso

rall.

Lento

pp

CRADLE SONG

Andrew Moore

CRANHAM

Malcolm Archer

Steady but flowing (♩ = 69)

CRANHAM

Noel Rawsthorne

Melody: 'Cranham' by Gustav Holst © Copyright Oxford University Press. Used by permission.

It is illegal to photocopy music.

DIX

Malcolm Archer

rall.

FOREST GREEN

Noel Rawsthorne

Melody: 'Forest Green', collected by Ralph Vaughan Williams © Copyright Oxford University Press. Used by permission.

73

GOD REST YOU MERRY, GENTLEMEN

Noel Rawsthorne

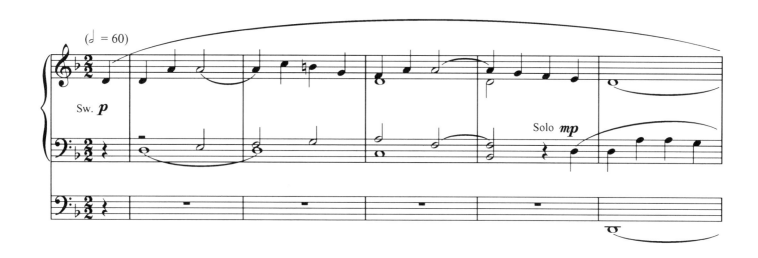

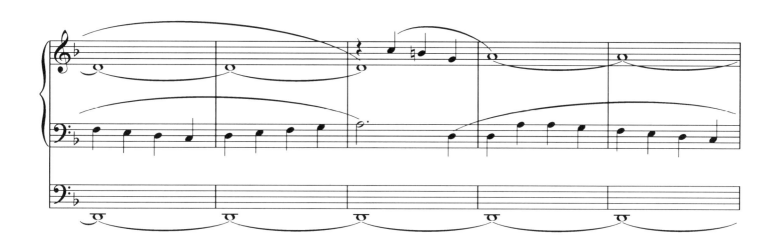

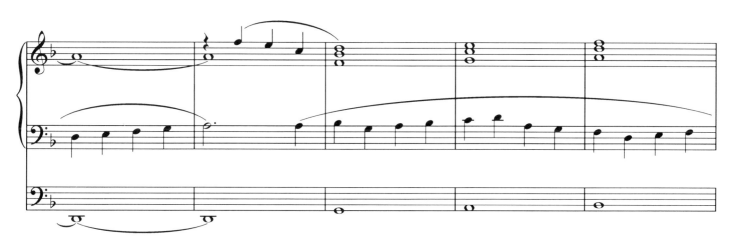

Sw. +
Reeds

3

ff

poco rall.

GREENSLEEVES

Noel Rawsthorne

HUMILITY

Christopher Tambling

Soft 16' to Sw.

IN DULCI JUBILO

Noel Rawsthorne

Gently flowing (♩. = 48)

INFANT HOLY

Andrew Fletcher

IRBY

Andrew Moore

IRBY

Noel Rawsthorne

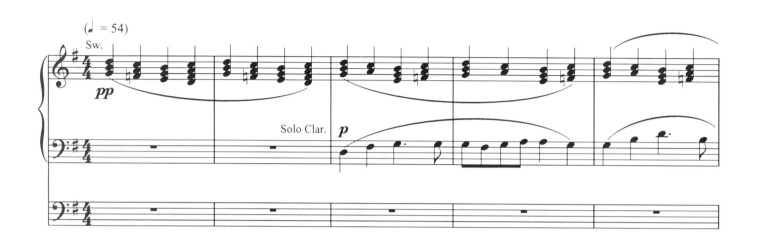

IRIS

Colin Hand

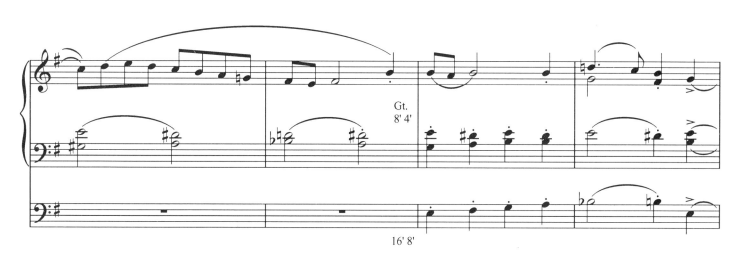

96

IRIS

Noel Rawsthorne

I SAW THREE SHIPS

Richard Proulx

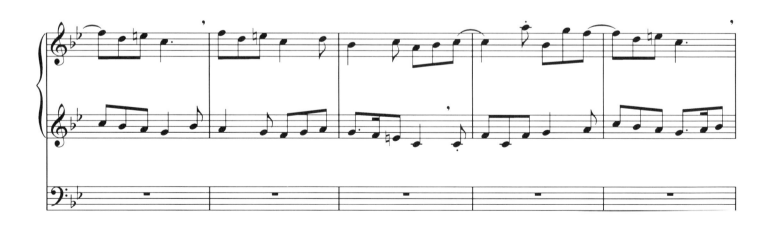

KINGS OF ORIENT

Noel Rawsthorne

MENDELSSOHN

Noel Rawsthorne

Broader

Solo Reeds

Gt.

MENDELSSOHN

Martin Setchell

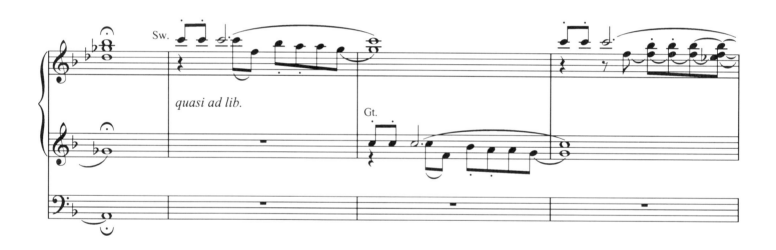

PUER NOBIS

Colin Mawby

Tuba

mf

cresc.

f

ff

rit.

fff

Full

117

PUER NOBIS

Noel Rawsthorne

QUEM PASTORES

Christopher Tambling

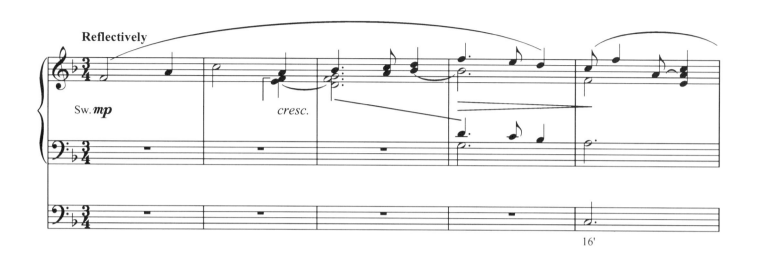

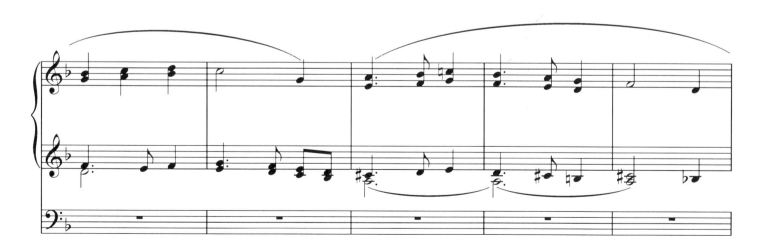

RESONET IN LAUDIBUS

Colin Mawby

127

for Dennis Hunt

RESONET IN LAUDIBUS

June Nixon

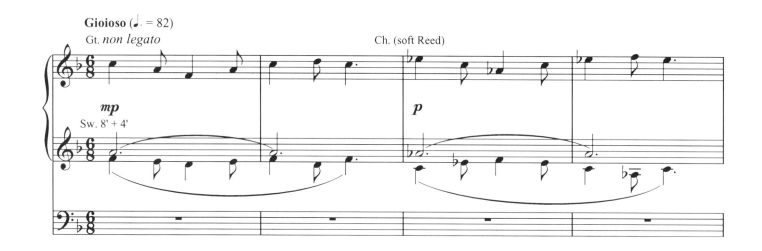

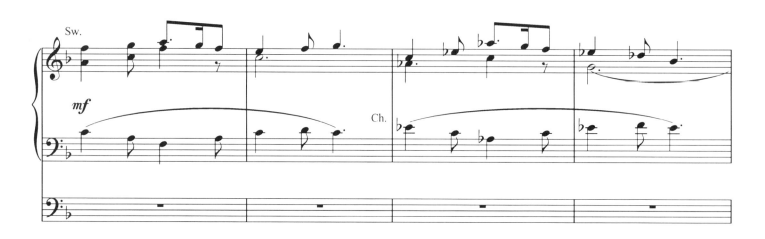

ROCKING

Philip Moore

Adagio espressivo ($\quad$ = c. 69)

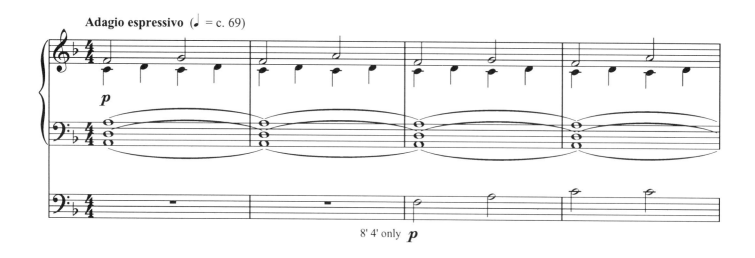

8' 4' only *p*

STILLE NACHT

Norman Warren

STUTTGART

Malcolm Archer

for James Lowry Esq. BA

SUSSEX CAROL

Quentin Thomas

142

for Ian Hunt

TEMPUS ADEST FLORIDUM

Paul Bryan

THE FIRST NOWELL

June Nixon

THE HOLLY AND THE IVY

Richard Proulx

Variation 2

($\downarrow$ = 76-80)

Man. I

Man. I: Fl. 8'+2'
Man. II: Soft Reed 8'

Man. II

16' 8'

150

poco rit.

151

WINCHESTER OLD

Andrew Moore

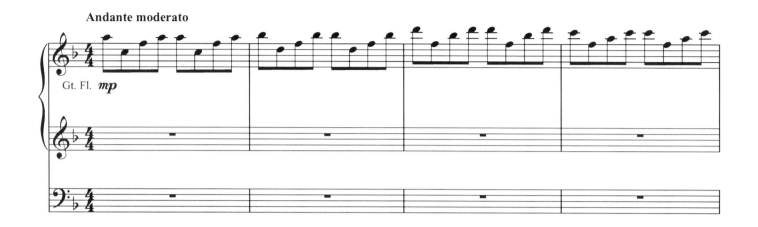

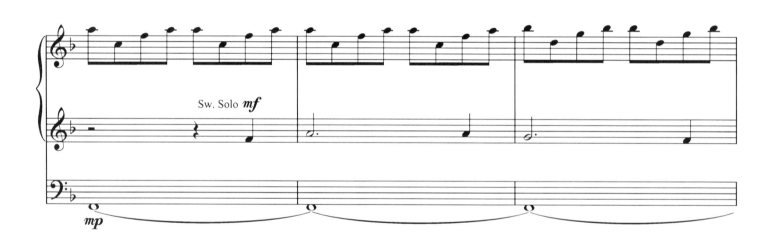

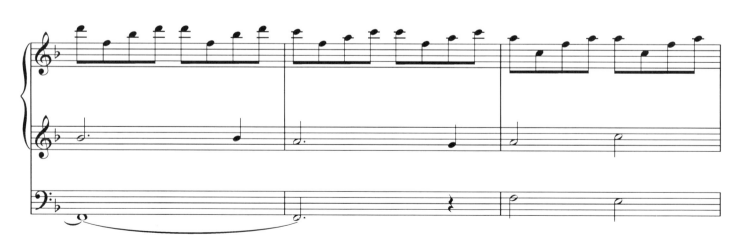

WINCHESTER OLD

Philip Moore

Verset 1
Un poco allegro (♩ = c. 80)

Verset 2
Un poco adagio (♩ = c. 63)

Verset 3

Andante maestoso ($\quarternote$ = c. 80)

YORKSHIRE

Noel Rawsthorne

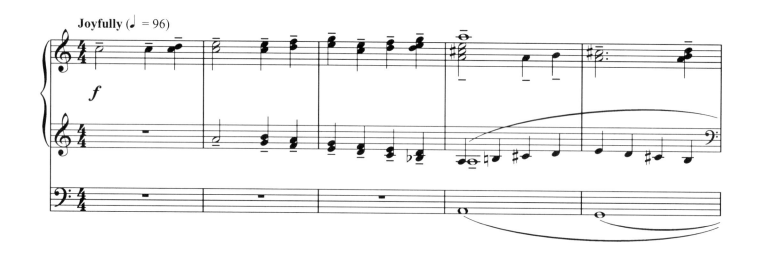

Lent & Holy Week

AUS DER TIEFE

June Nixon

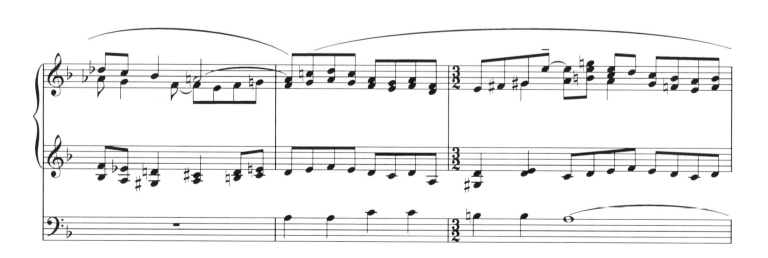

Meno mosso (♪ = 76)

rall.

allargando

+16'

BELMONT

Andrew Moore

CASWALL

Richard Lloyd

169

HORSLEY

Richard Shephard

173

PASSION CHORALE

Andrew Moore

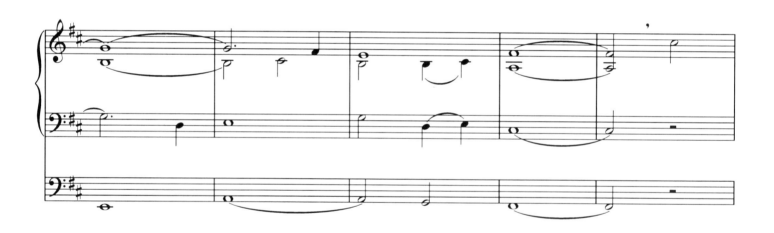

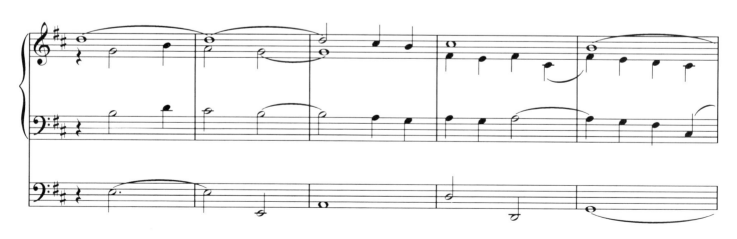

Sw. Soft Reed

PASSION CHORALE

William Lloyd Webber

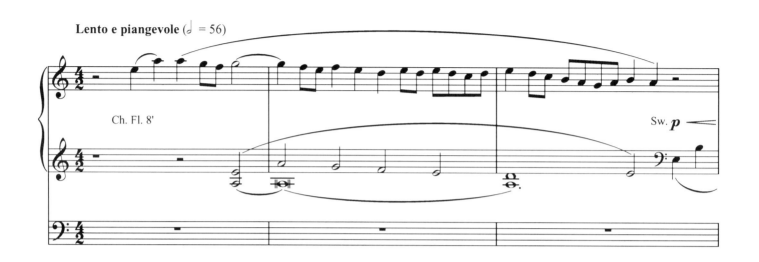

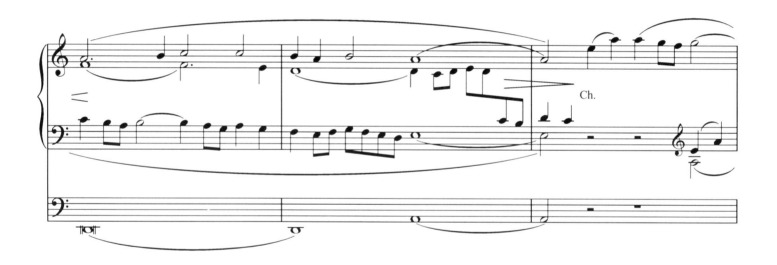

179

ROCKINGHAM

Rosalie Bonighton

ROCKINGHAM

Richard Proulx

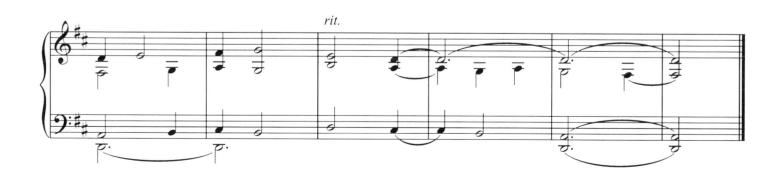

SONG 13 (CANTERBURY)

A.E. Floyd

for Bishop James A. Grant

SONG 13 (CANTERBURY)

June Nixon

Variation 2
Poco più mosso (♩. = 76)

Variation 3
Alla sarabanda (♩ = 92)

Variation 4

Animato (♩. = 66)

Sw. *mf*

Variation 5

Sonoramente (♩ = 72)

Variation 6

Lento (♩ = 84)

rall.   più lento

Sw.
Stgs. *pp*

ppp

193

SOUTHWELL

Colin Hand

Andante con rubato (♩ = c. 72)

16' 8'

ST BERNARD

Andrew Fletcher

rall.

poco marcato

ST THEODULPH

Andrew Moore

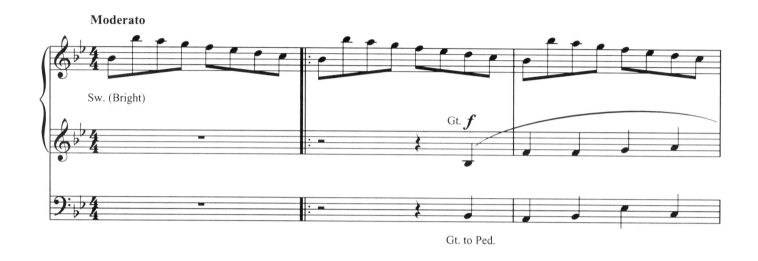

STABAT MATER

Alan Viner

Andante flessibile ($\quad$ = 68)

Sw. *mp*

16'+8' to Sw.

poco rit.

WERE YOU THERE

Christopher Tambling

Slowly and freely, with much feeling

- Sw. Oboe

- Gt. to Sw.

Ch. or Solo

Sw.

pp

WINCHESTER NEW

Andrew Moore

WINCHESTER NEW

William Lloyd Webber

Easter & Ascension

CHRIST AROSE

Christopher Tambling

217

EASTER HYMN

Noel Rawsthorne

poco a poco allargando al fine

Lento

EASTER HYMN

Christopher Tambling

ELLACOMBE

Philip Moore

Maestoso (♩ = c. 69)

ELLACOMBE

June Nixon

GELOB'T SEI GOTT

Andrew Gant

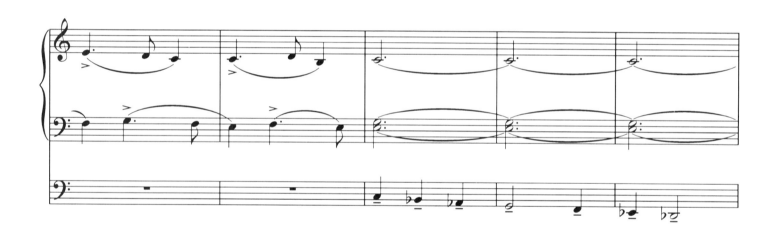

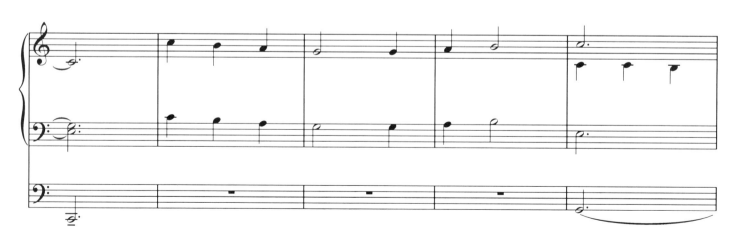

LLANFAIR

Andrew Moore

Allegro moderato (♩ = c. 84)

LUX EOI

Andrew Moore

MACCABAEUS

Noel Rawsthorne

NARENZA

Colin Mawby

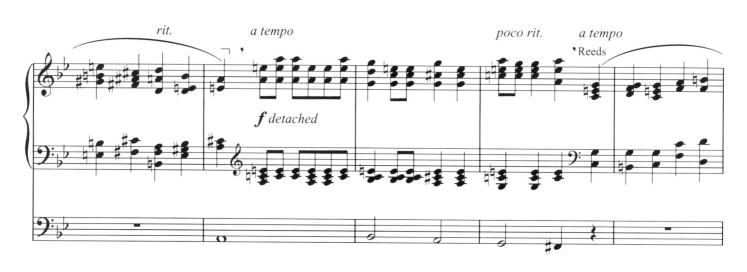

NOEL NOUVELET

Malcolm Archer

Sprightly (♩ = 96)

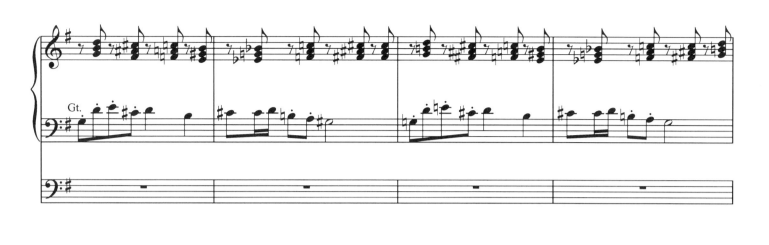

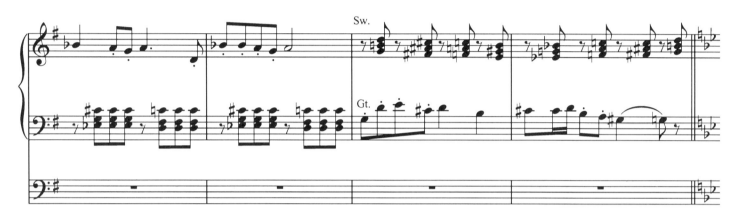

248

O FILII ET FILIAE

Colin Mawby

251

O FILII ET FILIAE

Christopher Tambling

Quasi fantasia

SALZBURG

Rosalie Bonighton

SAVANNAH

Rosalie Bonighton

SAVANNAH

Stanley Vann

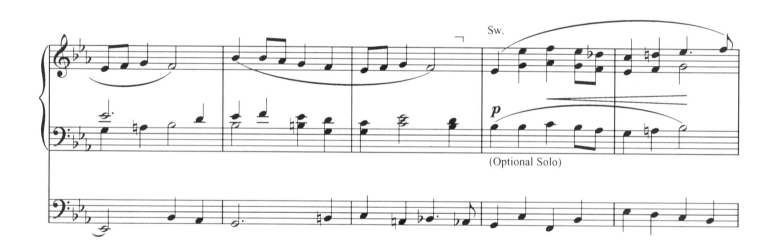

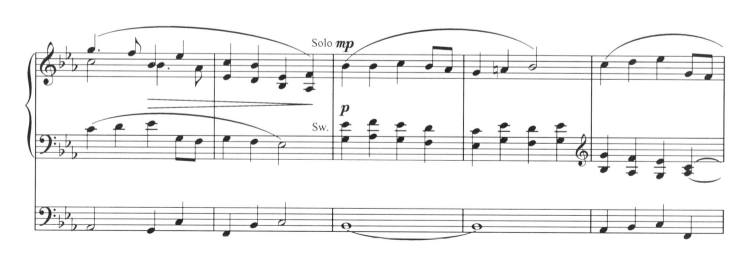

for Billy

ST ALBINUS

Paul Bryan

poco rall.

ST FULBERT

Richard Lloyd

ST FULBERT

Philip Moore

poco rall.

ST HELEN

Christopher Tambling

ST JOHN DAMASCENE

Noel Rawsthorne

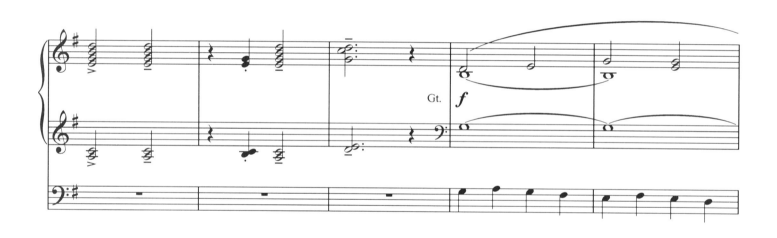

Tubas or Sw.

Gt.

276

to George Mitchell

THIS JOYFUL EASTERTIDE

Alan Ridout

279

VICTORY

Colin Hand

VICTORY

Noel Rawsthorne

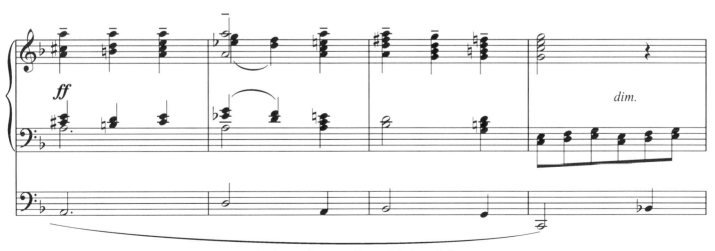

Pentecost

in memory of Helen

CAPETOWN

Paul Bryan

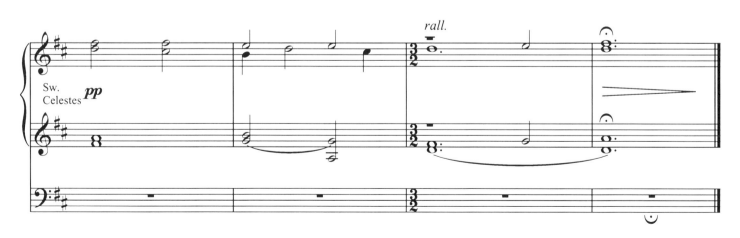

CARLISLE

Paul Bryan

Moderato (♩ = 70)

CHARITY

Richard Proulx

FARLEY CASTLE

June Nixon

TALLIS' ORDINAL

John Jordan

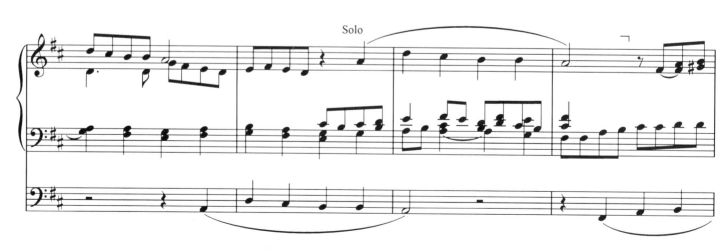

VENI, CREATOR SPIRITUS

Malcolm Archer

* *Alternatively, the strands of plainsong may be played on the Pedals.*
They should be free in tempo but the interludes in between in stricter time.

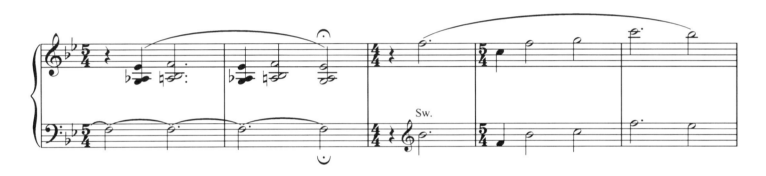

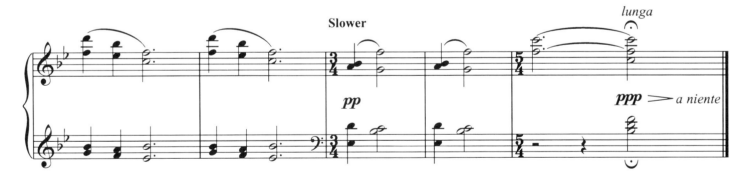

VENI, CREATOR SPIRITUS

Richard Proulx

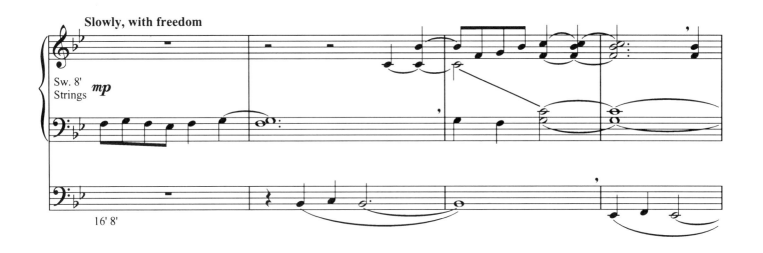

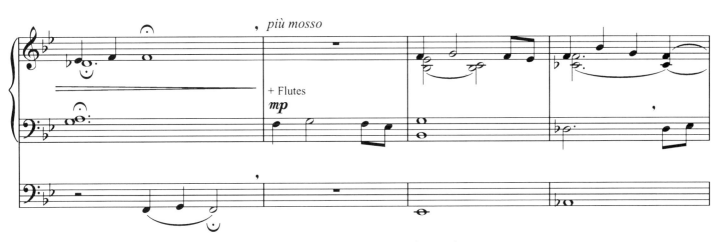

VENI, CREATOR SPIRITUS

Noel Rawsthorne

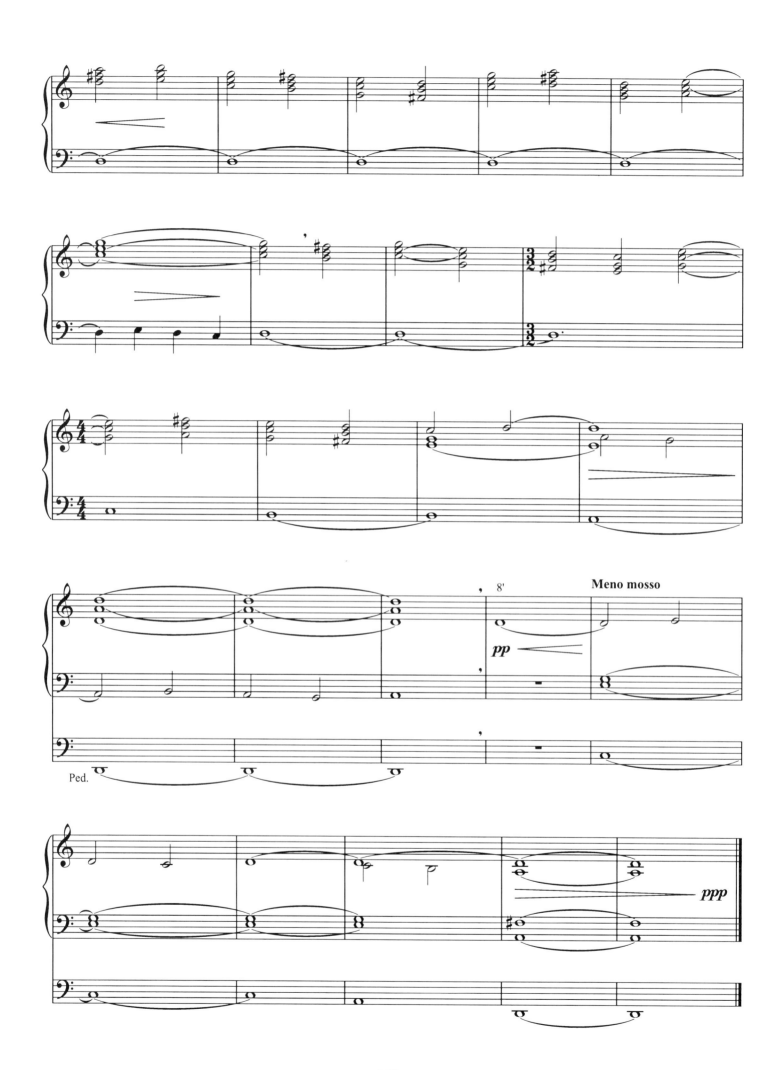

Trinity

NICAEA

John Marsh